Better Bass With...

Rockschool

www.rockschool.co.uk

Welcome To Bass Grade 2

Welcome to the Rockschool Bass Grade 2 pack. The book and CD contain everything needed to play bass in this grade. In the book you will find the exam scores in both standard bass notation and TAB. The accompanying CD has full stereo mixes of each tune, backing tracks to play along with for practice, tuning notes and spoken two bar count-ins to each piece. Handy tips on playing the pieces and the marking schemes can be found in the Guru's Guide on page 16. If you have any queries about this or any other Rockschool exam, please call us on **0845 460 4747**, email us at *info@rockschool.co.uk* or visit our website *www.rockschool.co.uk*. Good luck!

Level 1 Requirements for Grades 1, 2 & 3

The nine Rockschool grades are divided into four levels. These levels correspond to the levels of the National Qualifications Framework (NQF). Further details about the NQF can be found at *www.qca.org.uk/NQF*. Details of all Rockschool's accredited qualifications can be found at *www.qca.org.uk/openquals*.

Bass Grade 2 is part of Level 1. This Level is for players who are just starting out and who are looking to build a solid technical and stylistic foundation for their playing.

Grade 1: a player of Grade 1 standard should be able to play up to 32 bars of music using first position grooves composed of whole, half, quarter and eighth notes and associated rests, tied notes, and dotted half and quarter notes. Performances should include basic legato and staccato playing where marked.

Grade 2: in this grade you are beginning to acquire a range of physical and expressive techniques, including staccato and slides, as well as simple dynamics. In this grade you will also begin to work on your stylistic appreciation.

Grade 3: in this grade you will be encountering syncopated eighth and sixteenth notes as well as developing the palette of expressive techniques to include slapped and pulled notes, fretting hand vibrato, hammer ons and pull offs, slides and simple bends. The pieces of music are now longer, covering two pages and you should be developing your stylistic awareness, taking into account tone settings for each song..

Bass Exams at Grade 2

There are **two** types of exam that can be taken using this pack: a Grade Exam and a Performance Certificate.

Bass Grade 2 Exam: this is for players who want to develop performance and technical skills

Players wishing to enter for a Bass Grade 2 exam need to prepare **three** pieces of which **one** may be a free choice piece chosen from outside the printed repertoire. In addition you must prepare the technical exercises in the book, undertake either a sight reading test or an improvisation & interpretation test, take an ear test and answer general musicianship questions. Samples of these tests are printed in the book along with audio examples on the CD.

Bass Grade 2 Performance Certificate: this is for players who want to focus on performing in a range of styles

To enter for your Bass Grade 2 Performance Certificate you play pieces only. You can choose any **five** of the six tunes printed in this book, or you can choose to bring in up to **two** free choice pieces as long as they meet the standards set out by Rockschool. Free choice piece checklists for all grades can be found on the Rockschool website: *www.rockschool.co.uk*.

Bass Notation Explained

THE MUSICAL STAVE shows pitches and rhythms and is divided by lines into bars. Pitches are named after the first seven letters of the alphabet.

TABLATURE graphically represents the bass guitar fingerboard. Each horizontal line represents a string, and each number represents a fret.

4th string, 3rd fret

Fmaj7 chord in the 7th position

Ad lib. and *cont. sim.* sections are shown in slash notation

Definitions For Special Bass Guitar Notation

HAMMER ON: Pick the lower note, then sound the higher note by fretting it without picking.

PULL OFF: Pick the higher note then sound the lower note by lifting the finger without picking.

SLIDE: Pick the first note, then slide to the next with the same finger.

GLISSANDO: Pick the note and slide along the string in the direction indicated.

SLAP STYLE: Slap bass technique is indicated through the letters T (thumb) and P (pull).

TAPPING: Sound note by tapping the string – circles denote a picking hand tap, squares a fretting hand tap.

DEAD (GHOST) NOTES: Pick the string while the note is muted with the fretting hand.

NATURAL HARMONICS: Lightly touch the string above the indicated fret then pick to sound a harmonic.

 (accent) • Accentuate note (play it louder).

 (accent) • Accentuate note with great intensity.

 (staccato) • Shorten time value of note.

 • Fermata (Pause)

D.%. al Coda

• Go back to the sign (%), then play until the bar marked *To Coda* ⊕ then skip to the section marked ⊕ *Coda*.

D.C. al Fine

• Go back to the beginning of the song and play until the bar marked *Fine* (end).

• Repeat bars between signs.

• When a repeated section has different endings, play the first ending only the first time and the second ending only the second time.

Peanut Butter

Hussein Boon

Riff Raff

Deirdre Cartwright

M & C's Tune

Jason Woolley

Like It Is

John Eacott

Bass Grade 2

Hot Potarto

Henry Thomas

Blue Phones

Jason Woolley

Technical Exercises

In this section, the examiner will ask you to play a selection of exercises drawn from each of the three groups shown below. Groups A and B contain examples of the kinds of scales and arpeggios you can use when playing the pieces. In Group C you will be asked to prepare the exercise and play it to the backing track on the CD. You do not need to memorise the exercises (and can use the book in the exam) but the examiner will be looking for the speed of your response. The examiner will also give credit for the level of your musicality.

Groups A and B should be prepared in all of the following keys: A, G, C and B, and should be played at ♩ = 80. The examiner will give you this tempo in the exam.

Group A: Scales

1. Major scales. C major scale example shown

2. Natural minor scales. C natural minor scale example shown

3. Minor pentatonic scales. C minor pentatonic scale example shown

Group B: Arpeggios

1. Major arpeggios. C major arpeggio shown

2. Minor arpeggios. C minor arpeggio shown

Grade Exam and Performance Certificate Entry Form

Please complete the form below in BLOCK CAPITALS. Information given below will only be used by Rockschool for exam purposes and for Rockschool news. Completed application forms should be sent, along with a cheque made payable to 'Rockschool' for the appropriate fees, to:

Exam Entries, Rockschool, Evergreen House, 2-4 King Street, Twickenham, Middlesex, TW1 3RZ

1. Candidate's Details

Full Name (as it will appear on the certificate):

Date of Birth (DD/MM/YY)*:   Gender (M/F)*:   *This information is compulsory but will be used for statistical purposes only

Address:

Postcode:

Telephone No: Mobile No:

Email address:

☐ (Please tick) **Yes!** I would like to receive all correspondence from Rockschool via email (with the exception of certificates and mark sheets which will be posted). *Rockschool will NOT circulate your email address to any third parties.*

2. Your Examination

Type of Exam (Grade or Performance Certificate):   Grade:

Instrument: *If you are applying for multiple examinations, please continue below:*

Type of Exam: Instrument: Grade:

Type of Exam: Instrument: Grade:

Period (A/B/C)*:   *Refer to our website for exam periods and closing dates*

Preferred Town for Examination (*Refer to our website for a list of current towns with Rockschool examination centres**):

*Rockschool will endeavour to place you at your preferred town, but cannot guarantee this

Please state any dates that are IMPOSSIBLE for you to attend*:

*It is not guaranteed that we can avoid these dates

3. Additional information

Drum Candidates. Do you require a left-handed kit?

Will you be bringing your own kit (Grades 6,7,8 only)?   If 'no' Rockschool will provide a drum kit.

Popular Piano Candidates. Will you be bringing your own keyboard?

If 'no', Rockschool can provide either a keyboard or a piano. Please indicate which you prefer :

Special Needs Candidates. Please include a supporting letter with your application explaining your requirements.

All Candidates. If there is any additional information you consider relevant, please attach a note to your application.

4. Fees – *For current exam prices please refer to our website, www.rockschool.co.uk or call us on 0845 460 4747*

Fee enclosed:

Cheque Number: PLEASE WRITE CANDIDATE NAME ON BACK OF CHEQUE

Teacher's Exam Entry Form

Teachers wishing to enter **grade exams** and **performance certificates** on behalf of their students should complete the form below in BLOCK CAPITALS. Information given will only be used by Rockschool for exam purposes and for Rockschool news. You can get up to date information on examination prices from **www.rockschool.co.uk** or by ringing the Rockschool helpline on **0845 460 4747**. Completed application forms should be sent, along with a cheque made payable to '**Rockschool**' for the appropriate fees, to:

Exam Entries, Rockschool, Evergreen House, 2-4 King Street, Twickenham, Middlesex, TW1 3RZ

1. Teacher's Details

Title (Mr/Mrs/Ms etc):   Full Name:

Address:

Postcode:

Telephone No: Mobile No:

Email address:

For school entries please include your NCN (National Centre Number):

☐ (Please tick) **Yes!** I would like to receive all correspondence from Rockschool via email (with the exception of certificates and mark sheets which will be posted). *Rockschool will NOT circulate your email address to any third parties.*

2. Examination Details and Fees

*For grade exams, please write 'G' and the grade number in the Grade box (e.g. **G6** for Grade 6). For performance certificates, please write 'PC' and the grade number in the Grade box (e.g. **PC4** for Performance Certificate Grade 4).* †*For examination periods refer to our website. Continue on separate sheet if necessary.*

FOR SPECIAL NEEDS CANDIDATES PLEASE ATTACH A SUPPORTING LETTER WITH DETAILS.

Candidate's Name (as it will appear on the certificate)	Date of Birth	Gender (M/F)	Instrument	Grade*	Period†	Fee (£)
1.	DD MM YYYY					
2.	DD MM YYYY					
3.	DD MM YYYY					
4.	DD MM YYYY					
5.	DD MM YYYY					
6.	DD MM YYYY					
7.	DD MM YYYY					
8.	DD MM YYYY					
9.	DD MM YYYY					
10.	DD MM YYYY					
11.	DD MM YYYY					
12.	DD MM YYYY					
					Total fees enclosed £	

Preferred Town for Examination (*Refer to our website for a list of current towns with Rockschool examination centres**):

*Rockschool will endeavour to place your candidates at your preferred town, but cannot guarantee this

Please list dates your candidate(s) **cannot** attend*:

*It is not guaranteed that we can avoid these dates

Band Exam Entry Form

You can enter for one of the following band exams (1 Guitar player, 1 Bass player, 1 Drummer) using Rockschool materials: * *Level One (Grade 3 repertoire)* * *Level Two (Grade 5 repertoire)* *Level Three (Grade 8 repertoire)* Please complete the form below in BLOCK CAPITALS. Information given will only be used by Rockschool for exam purposes and for Rockschool news. Completed application forms should be sent, along with a cheque made payable to 'Rockschool' for the appropriate fees, to:

Exam Entries, Rockschool, Evergreen House, 2-4 King Street, Twickenham, Middlesex, TW1 3RZ

---

1. Band's Details

GUITARIST Full Name (as it will appear on the certificate):

Date of Birth (DD/MM/YY)*:   Gender (M/F)*:

BASSIST Full Name (as it will appear on the certificate):

Date of Birth (DD/MM/YY)*:   Gender (M/F)*:

DRUMMER Full Name (as it will appear on the certificate):

Date of Birth (DD/MM/YY)*:   Gender (M/F)*:

*This information is compulsory but will be used for statistical purposes only

---

2. Band's Main Contact Details

Main Contact's Name:

Address:

                                              Postcode:

Telephone No: Mobile No:

Email address:

☐ (Please tick) **Yes!** I would like to receive all correspondence from Rockschool via email (with the exception of certificates and mark sheets which will be posted). *Rockschool will NOT circulate your email address to any third parties.*

---

3. Your Examination — *If you are applying for multiple exams, please use a separate form for each*

Exam Level (One/Two/Three):

Period (A/B/C)*:   *Refer to our website for exam periods and closing dates*

Preferred Town for Examination (*Refer to our website for a list of current towns with Rockschool examination centres*):

Rockschool will endeavour to place you at your preferred town, but cannot guarantee this

Please state any dates that are IMPOSSIBLE for you to attend*:

It is not guaranteed that we can avoid these dates

Additional Information *If there is any additional information you consider relevant (e.g. band members with special needs) please attach a separate sheet explaining your requirements.*

---

4. Fees — *For current exam prices please refer to our website, www.rockschool.co.uk or call us on 0845 460 4747*

Fee enclosed:

Cheque Number: PLEASE WRITE CANDIDATES' NAMES ON BACK OF CHEQUE

ROCKSCHOOL HELPLINE: 0845 460 4747
email: info@rockschool.co.uk   website: www.rockschool.co.uk

ROCKSCHOOL RESOURCES

At Rockschool we recognise the importance of keeping teachers and learners up to date with developments. Below are listed the qualifications and resources on offer. If you have any questions, please contact us through the relevant email address, or phone us on **0845 460 4747**.

PERFORMANCE DIPLOMAS

Music Performance Diploma (DipRSL Perf) at Level 4

Music Performance Licentiate (LRSL Perf) at Level 6

The Rockschool Performance Diplomas provide flexible, vocationally relevant qualifications for experienced or skilled performers of popular music.

diplomas@rockschool.co.uk

TEACHING DIPLOMAS

Teaching Diploma (DipRSL) at Level 4
Teaching Diploma (LRSL) at Level 6

The Rockschool Teaching Diplomas have been devised for instrumentalists, vocalists and music technologists who would like to attain a teaching qualification without having to attend a course or write essays. The diplomas focus on the practicalities of teaching and are neither genre nor instrument specific.

diplomas@rockschool.co.uk

MUSIC PRACTITIONERS QUALIFICATIONS

Rockschool/ATM
14-19 Diploma
Compatible

These flexible, vocationally relevant popular music qualifications will provide learners with the necessary skills to develop realistic employment opportunities in the music industry.

qualifications@rockschool.co.uk

COMPANION GUIDES

Sight Reading (Grades 1-8)
Improvisation & Interpretation (Grades 1-5)
QSPs (Grades 6-8)
Ear Tests (Grades 1-8)
GMQs (Grades 1-8)

A must for any music teacher or self-taught musician using the Rockschool grade system. Rockschool Companion Guides contain examples of the exercises you will encounter in an exam along with tips on how best to perform.

info@rockschool.co.uk

Companion Guides available for purchase through **www.musicroom.com**

GUITAR DVDS

Following DVDs available:
Grades Debut & 1
Grade 2
Grade 3

Perfect for anyone working through the Rockschool grades, Rockschool DVDs include instructional lessons on how to make the most of the pieces and technical exercises required in your exams.

info@rockschool.co.uk

DVDs available for purchase through **www.musicroom.com**

COMING SOON...REPERTOIRE BOOKS

Rockschool Repertoire Books contain popular songs from rock through to indie. **Drums Grades 1 to 3** will be available from October 2008.

info@rockschool.co.uk

Repertoire Books soon available for purchase through **www.musicroom.com**

Group C: Bassline

Prepare the following bassline in the key shown. You will perform this exercise in the exam to the backing track on the CD. The riff shown in bar 1 should be played in the same shape in each of the subsequent bars as indicated. The root note of the riff is shown in each bar.

Sight Reading

In this section you have a choice between **either** a sight reading test **or** an improvisation & interpretation test (see facing page). Printed below is the type of sight reading test you are likely to encounter in the exam. The piece will be composed in the style of blues or rock. The examiner will allow you 90 seconds to prepare it and will set the tempo for you on a metronome. The tempo is ♩ = 70.

Improvisation & Interpretation

Printed below is an example of the type of improvisation & interpretation test you are likely to encounter in the exam. You will be asked to play an improvised bassline over a backing track lasting four bars in the style of blues or rock played by the examiner on CD. You will be allowed 30 seconds to prepare and the examiner will set the tempo. You will then be allowed to practise through one playing of the test on the CD before playing it a second time for the exam. This test is continuous with a one bar count in at the beginning and after the practice session. This test is continuous. The tempo is ♩=70.

Ear Tests

There are two ear tests in this grade. The examiner will play each test to you on CD. You will find one example of each type of test you will be given in the exam printed below.

Test 1: Melodic Recall

You will be asked to play back on your bass a simple melody of not more than two bars composed from notes of the C major scale. You will be given the tonic note and told the starting note, and you will hear the test twice with a drum backing. There will then be a short break for you to practise the test and then the test will recommence and you will be required to play the melody with the drum backing. This test is continuous. The tempo is ♩=70.

Test 2: Rhythmic Recall

You will be asked to play back the given simple two bar rhythm on the E string of your bass. You will hear the rhythm played twice and then you will play it back to the examiner. The tempo is ♩=70.

General Musicianship Questions

You will be asked five General Musicianship Questions at the end of the exam. The examiner will ask questions based on pieces you have played in the exam. Some of the theoretical topics can be found in the Technical Exercises.

Topics:

i)   Music theory
ii) Knowledge of your instrument

The music theory questions will cover the recognition of the following at this grade:

Note pitches	Dynamic markings (*p*, *mp*, *mf* and *mf*)
Note values	Repeat markings
Rests	Accents, staccato and vibrato
Time Signatures	Hammer on and pull off
Key Signatures	Notes on the stave

Knowledge of the construction of the following arpeggios

Major
Minor

The instrument knowledge questions will cover the following topics at this grade:

Plugging into the amplifier and the bass
Volume and tone adjustments on the bass
Note names of open strings

Knowledge of parts of the bass:

Fretboard, neck, body, tuning pegs, nut, pickups, bridge, pickup selectors, scratchplate and jack socket

Knowledge of main bass makes.

Questions on all these topics will be based on pieces played by you in the exam. Tips on how to approach this part of the exam can be found in the Rockschool Companion Guide and on the Rockschool website: *www.rockschool.co.uk*.

The Guru's Guide To Bass Grade 2

This section contains some handy hints compiled by Rockschool's Bass Guru to help you get the most out of the performance pieces. Do feel free to adapt the tunes to suit your playing style. Remember, these tunes are your chance to show your musical imagination and personality.

The TAB fingerings are suggestions only. Feel free to use different neck positions as they suit you. Please also note that any solos featured in the full mixes are not meant to be indicative of the standard required for the grade.

Bass Grade 2 Tunes

Rockschool tunes help you play the hit tunes you enjoy. The pieces have been written by top pop and rock composers and players according to style specifications drawn up by Rockschool.

The tunes printed here fall into two categories. The first category can be called the 'contemporary mainstream' and features current styles in today's charts. The second category of pieces consists of 'roots styles', those classic grooves and genres which influence every generation of performers.

CD full mix track 1, backing track 8: Peanut Butter

This techno-electronic piece is driven forward by a four note eighth note riff, all played on the same note one of which is an octave above the others, a bass technique common in many styles including funk. This pattern is played in a shifting fret positions: note the changes to the riff in bars 22 and 23 where the octave falls in the second and not the third note. Other features to watch out for are the dynamics, changes in volume from section to section and the eighth note rests .

Composer: Hussein Boon.

CD full mix track 2, backing track 9: Riff Raff

The bassline of this metal track features quite a tricky opening that is repeated (note the change in dynamics from loud to medium loud the second time through). Thereafter, the bass part is quite sparse and dynamically moves from quiet to loud over the space of ten bars. This part also features some simple syncopations in bars 25-32 where notes are tied across bars.

Composer: Deirdre Cartwright.

CD full mix track 3, backing track 10: M and C's Tune

This modern r'n'b piece begins with a four bar riff played mainly in eighth notes. The main groove is likewise played in eighth notes and made interesting by the use of rests to break up the rhythm. The middle section starts on each bar with a dotted quarter note. Look out for the subtle changes in dynamics from bar to bar in this section. Towards the end of the song there are several bars of quarter notes which should be played evenly.

Composer: Jason Woolley.

CD full mix track 4, backing track 11: Like It Is

The opening bars of this shuffle blues track show a contrast in dynamics from bar to bar from loud to soft. Most of the remainder of this repeated section is made up of a flowing quarter note groove known as 'walking bass' on account of its even feel. This feel is maintained for most of the rest of the song, apart from two bars of stops towards the end. Try to make the ascending-descending line have musical shape. The rests in bars 20 & 22 are very important.

Composer: John Eacott.

CD full mix track 5, backing track 12: Hot Potarto

This is funk piece with a fun groove. The opening sixteen bars, played as two sets of repeated eight bars, are essentially the same groove with slight variations to the pattern; the second set of eight bars has some string skipping but this should not be too arduous as the first note in each case is played on an open string. The middle section is played three times, as shown by the repeats, but the following two bars are the resolution played in the same groove. The remainder of the song again varies the theme of the opening, and the last four bars have some simple syncopations and some more string skipping. There is use of chromatic work here so make sure it is clearly heard.

Composer: Henry Thomas.

CD full mix track 6, backing track 13: Blue Phones

This modern guitar pop tune features pedal eighth notes for the intro before moving onto a groove that mixes these with some simple syncopations. There is some octave note work in places (in bars 12, 13 and 17). The second half of the song is mainly a restatement of the first half intro. The part can be shaped by making the most of the dynamic contrasts (soft at the beginning and louder during the main part of the song).

Composer: Jason Woolley.

CD Musicians:

Bass: Deirdre Cartwright; Keith Airey; Hussein Boon
Bass: Henry Thomas; Jason Woolley
Drums: Peter Huntington; Noam Lederman
Keyboards and programming: Alastair Gavin

Bass Grade 2 Marking Schemes

The table below shows the marking scheme for the Bass Grade 2 exam.

ELEMENT	PASS	MERIT	DISTINCTION
Piece 1	13 out of 20	15 out of 20	17+ out of 20
Piece 2	13 out of 20	15 out of 20	17+ out of 20
Piece 3	13 out of 20	15 out of 20	17+ out of 20
Technical Exercises	11 out of 15	12–13 out of 15	14+ out of 15
Either Sight Reading *or* Improvisation & Interpretation	6 out of 10	7–8 out of 10	9+ out of 10
Ear Tests	6 out of 10	7–8 out of 10	9+ out of 10
General Musicianship Questions	3 out of 5	4 out of 5	5 out of 5
Total Marks	**Pass: 65%+**	**Merit: 75%+**	**Distinction: 85%+**

The table below shows the marking scheme for the Bass Grade 2 Performance Certificate

ELEMENT	PASS	MERIT	DISTINCTION
Piece 1	14 out of 20	16 out of 20	18+ out of 20
Piece 2	14 out of 20	16 out of 20	18+ out of 20
Piece 3	14 out of 20	16 out of 20	18+ out of 20
Piece 4	14 out of 20	16 out of 20	18+ out of 20
Piece 5	14 out of 20	16 out of 20	18+ out of 20
Total Marks	**Pass: 70%+**	**Merit: 80%+**	**Distinction: 90%+**

Entering Rockschool Exams

Entering a Rockschool exam is easy. Please read through these instructions carefully before filling in the exam entry form. Information on current exam fees can be obtained from Rockschool by ringing 0845 460 4747 or by logging on to our website *www.rockschool.co.uk.*

• You should enter for your exam when you feel ready.

• You can enter for any one of three examination periods. These are shown below with their closing dates.

PERIOD	DURATION	CLOSING DATE
Period A	1st February to 15th March	1st December
Period B	1st May to 31st July	1st April
Period C	23rd October to 15th December	1st October

These dates will apply from 1st September 2006 until further notice

• Please complete the form giving the information required. Please fill in the type and level of exam, the instrument, along with the period and year. Finally, fill in the fee box with the appropriate amount. You can obtain up to date information on all Rockschool exam fees from the website: *www.rockschool.co.uk.* You should send this form with a cheque or postal order (payable to Rockschool Ltd) to the address shown on the order form. **Please also indicate on the form whether or not you would like to receive notification via email.**

• Applications received after the expiry of the closing date may be accepted subject to the payment of an additional fee.

• When you enter an exam you will receive from Rockschool an acknowledgement letter or email containing a copy of our exam regulations.

• Rockschool will allocate your entry to a centre and you will receive notification of the exam, showing a date, location and time as well as advice of what to bring to the centre. We endeavour to give you four weeks' notice of your exam.

• You should inform Rockschool of any cancellations or alterations to the schedule as soon as you can as it is usually not possible to transfer entries from one centre, or one period, to another without the payment of an additional fee.

• Please bring your music book and CD to the exam. You may not use photocopied music, nor the music used by someone else in another exam. The examiner will sign each book during each examination. You may be barred from taking an exam if you use someone else's music.

• You should aim to arrive for your Grade 2 exam fifteen minutes before the time stated on the schedule.

• Each Grade 2 exam is scheduled to last for 15 minutes. You can use a small proportion of this time to tune up and get ready.

• Two to three weeks after the exam you will receive a copy of the examiner's mark sheet. Every successful player will receive a Rockschool certificate of achievement.